THE EYES OF ASIA

Books by Rudyard Kipling

Actions and Reactions
Brushwood Boy, The
Captains Courageous
Collected Verse
Day's Work, The
Departmental Ditties and Ballads and Barrack-Room Ballads
Diversity of Creatures, A
Eyes of Asia, The
Five Nations, The
France at War
From Sea to Sea
History of England, A
Jungle Book, The
Jungle Book, Second
Just So Song Book
Just So Stories
Kim
Kipling Stories and Poems Every Child Should Know
Kipling Birthday Book, The

Life's Handicap: Being Stories of Mine Own People
Light That Failed, The
Many Inventions
Naulahka, The (With Wolcott Balestier)
Plain Tales from the Hills
Puck of Pook's Hill
Rewards and Fairies
Sea Warfare
Seven Seas, The
Soldier Stories
Soldiers Three, The Story of the Gadsbys, and In Black and White
Song of the English, A
Songs From Books
Stalky & Co.
They
Traffics and Discoveries
Under the Deodars, The Phantom 'Rickshaw, and Wee Willie Winkie
With the Night Mail

THE
EYES OF ASIA

BY
RUDYARD KIPLING

GARDEN CITY   NEW YORK
DOUBLEDAY, PAGE & COMPANY
1919

CONTENTS

A RETIRED GENTLEMAN

A RETIRED GENTLEMAN

From Bishen Singh Saktawut, Subedar Major, 215th Indurgurh [Todd's] Rajputs, now at Lyndhurst, Hampshire, England, this letter is sent to Madhu Singh, Sawant, Risaldar Major [retired] 146th [Dublana] Horse, on his fief which he holds under the Thakore Sahib of Pech at Bukani by the River, near Chiturkaira, Kotah, Rajputana, written in the fifth month of the year 1916, English count.

HAVING experienced five months of this war, I became infected with fever and a strong coldness of the stomach [rupture]. The doctor ordered me out of it altogether. They have also cut me with knives for a wound on my leg. It is now healed but the strength is gone, and it is very frightened of the ground. I have been in many hospitals for a long time. At this present I am living in a hospital for Indian troops in a forest-reservation called "New," which was established by a King's order in ages past. There is no order for my return to India. I do not desire it. My Regiment has now gone out of France—to Egypt, or Africa. My officer Sahibs are for the most part dead or in hospitals. During a railway journey when two people sit side by side for two hours one feels the absence of the other when he alights. How great then was my anguish at being severed from my Regiment after thirty-three years! Now, however, I am finished. If I return to India I cannot drill the new men between my two crutches. I should subsist in my village on my wound-pension among old and young who have never seen war. Here

I have great consideration. Though I am useless they are patient with me.

Having knowledge of the English tongue, I am sometimes invited to interpret between those in the hospital for the Indian troops and visitors of high position. I advance eminent visitors, such as relatives of Kings and Princes into the presence of the Colonel Doctor Sahib. I enjoy a small room apart from the hospital wards. I have a servant. The Colonel Doctor Sahib examines my body at certain times. I am forbidden to stoop even for my crutches. They are instantly restored to me by orderlies and my friends among the English. I come and go at my pleasure where I will, and my presence is solicited by the honourable.

You say I made a mistake to join the war at the end of my service? I have endured five months of it. Come you out and endure two and a half. You are three years younger than I. Why do you sit at home and drill new men? Remember:

> The Brahman who steals,
> The widow who wears ornaments,
> The Rajput who avoids the battle,
> Are only fit for crows' meat.

You write me that this is a war for young men? The old are not entirely useless. The Badshah [the King] himself gave me the medal for fetching in my captain from out of the wires upon my back. That work caused me the coldness in my stomach. Old men should not do coolie-work. Your cavalry were useless in France. Infantry can fight in this war—not cavalry. It is as impossible for us to get out of our trenches and exterminate the enemy as it is for the enemy to attack us. Doubtless the cavalry brigades will show what they are made of in Egypt or Persia. This business in France is all Artillery work and mines. The blowing up of the Chitoree Bastion when Arjoon went to Heaven waving his sword, as the song says, would not be noticed in the noise of this war.

The nature of the enemy is to go to earth and flood us with artillery of large weight. When we were in the trenches it was a burden. When we rested in the villages we found great ease. As to our food, it was like a bunnia's marriage-feast. Everything given, nothing counted. Some of us —especially among your cavalry—grew so fat that they were compelled to wrestle to keep thin. This is because there was no marching.

The nature of the enemy is to commit shame upon women and children, and to defile the shrines of his own faith with his own dung. It is done by him as a drill. We believed till then they were some sort of caste apart from the rest. We did not know they were outcaste. Now it is established by the evidence of our senses. They attack on all fours running like apes. They are specially careful for their faces. When death is certain to them they offer gifts and repeat the number of their children. They are very good single shots from cover.

It is the nature of the enemy to shower seductions from out of their air-machines on our troops in the lines. They promised such as would desert that they would become Rajahs among them. Some of the men went over to see if this were true. No report came back. In this way we cleaned out five bad characters from our Company exactly as it used to be in the little wars on the Border. May the enemy be pleased with them! No man of any caste disgraced our Regiment.

The nature of the enemy in this war is like the Nat [juggler] who is compelled to climb a pole for his belly's sake. If he does not climb he starves. If he stops he falls down. This is my thought concerning the enemy.

Now that our troops have gone out of France, the war is entirely between the enemy and the English, etc., etc. Both sides accordingly increased the number and the size of their guns. The new wounded officers in the English hospital say that the battles of even yesterday are not to be compared with the battle of to-day. Tell this to those who have returned and who boast. Only fools will desire more war when this war is ended. Their reward will be an instant extinction on account of the innumerable quantity of arms, munitions, etc., etc., which will be left in the hands of the experts. Those who make war henceforward will be as small jackals fighting beneath the feet of elephants. This Government has abundance of material, and fresh strength is added every hour. Let there be no mistake. The foolish have been greatly deceived in these matters by the nature of the English which is in the highest degree deceptive. Everything is done and spoken upside-down in this country of the English. He who has a thousand says: "It is but a scant hundred." The possessor of palaces says: "It is a hut," and the rest in proportion. Their boast is not to boast. Their greatness is to make themselves very small. They draw a curtain in front of all they do. It is as difficult to look upon the naked face of their achievements as in our country upon the faces of women.

It is not true there is no caste in England. The mark of the high castes, such as Ul or Baharun [Earl or Baron] is that they can perform any office, such as handling the dead, wounds, blood, etc., without loss of caste. The Maharanee of the Nurses in the English Hospital which is near our

Hospital is by caste Baharanee [Baroness].
I resort thither daily for society and enlightenment on the habits of this people.
The high castes are forbidden to show
curiosity, appetite, or fear in public places.
In this respect they resemble troops on
parade. Their male children are beaten
from their ninth year to their seventeenth
year, by men with sticks. Their women
are counted equal with their men. It is
reckoned as disgraceful for a Baharanee
to show fear when lights are extinguished
in the hospital on account of bomb-dropping
air-ships, as for an Ul to avoid battle.
They do not blacken each other's faces by
loud abuse, but by jests spoken in a small
voice.

The nature of the young men of high
caste is as the nature of us Rajputs. They
do not use opium, but they delight in horses,
and sport and women, and are perpetually
in debt to the moneylender. They shoot

partridge and they are forced to ride foxes because there are no wild pig here. They know nothing of hawking or quail-fighting, but they gamble up to the hilt on all occasions and bear losses laughing. Their card-play is called Baraich [Bridge?]. They belittle their own and the achievements of their friends, so long as that friend faces them. In his absence they extol his deeds. They are of cheerful countenance. When they jest, they respect honour. It is so also with their women. The Nurses in the Hospital of my Baharanee where I resort for society jest with me as daughters with a father. They say that they will be stricken with grief if I return to India. They call me Dada which is father also in their tongue. Though I am utterly useless they are unwearied of me. They themselves hasten to restore me my crutches when I let them fall. None of these women lament their dead openly. The eldest son of my Baharanee at the English Hospital where I am made welcome, was slain in battle. The next morning after the news my Baharanee let loose the plate-pianos [turned on the gramophones] for the delectation of the wounded. It comes into my mind to suggest to you that our women are unable to stand by themselves.

When the Badshah commanded me to his Palace to receive the medal, I saw all the wonders and entertainments of the city of London. There was neither trouble nor expense. My Baharanee gave orders I should inhabit her own house in that city. It was in reality a palace filled with carpets, gilt furniture, marbles, mirrors, silks, velvets, carvings, etc., etc. Hot water ran in silver pipes to my very bedside. The perfumed baths were perpetually renewed. When it rained daily I walked in a glass pavilion filled with scented flowers. I inhabited here ten days. Though I was utterly useless they were unwearied of me. A companion was found me. He was a Risaldar of Dekkani Horse, a man of family, wounded in the arms. We two received our medals together. We saw the King's Palace, and the custom of the Guard Mount in the mornings daily. Their drill is like stone walls, but the nature of the English music is without any meaning. We two saw the great temple, Seyn Pol [St. Paul's?], where their dead are. It is as a country enclosed in a house. My companion ascended to the very roof-top and saw all the city. We are nothing beside these people. We two also saw the Bird Garden [Zoological Gardens] where they studiously preserve all sorts of wild animals, even down to jackals and green parrots. It is the nature of the English to consider all created beings as equal. The Badshah himself wears khaki. His son the Shahzada is a young man who inhabits the trenches except when he is forbidden. He is a keen son of the sword.

It is true that trains run underneath the city in all directions. We descended into the earth upon a falling platform [lift] and travelled. The stopping-places are as close as beads on a thread. The doors of the carriages are guarded with gates that strike out sideways like cobras. Each sitter is allowed a space upon a divan of yellow canework. When the divans are full the surplus hang from the roof by leathers. Though our carriage was full, place was made for us. At the end of our journey the train was halted beyond its lawful time that we might come forth at ease. The trains were full of English soldiers. All castes of the English are now soldiers. They are become like us Rajputs—as many people so many soldiers.

We two saw houses, shops, carriages, and crowds till our souls were broken. The succeeding days were as the first, without intermission. We begged at last to be excused from the sight of the multitudes and the height of the houses.

We two agreed that understanding is most needful in this present age. We in India must get education before all things. Hereafter we Rajputs must seriously consider our arrangements in all respects—in our houses as well as in our fields, etc., etc. Otherwise we become nothing. We have been deceived by the nature of the English. They have not at any time shown us anything of their possessions or their performances. We are not even children beside them. They have dealt with us as though they were themselves children talking *chotee boli* [little talk]. In this manner the ill-informed have been misled. Nothing is known in India of the great strength of this people. Make that perfectly clear to all fools. Why should we who serve the Government have the blood of the misinformed on our heads when they behave foolishly? This people have all the strength. There is no reason except the nature of the English that anything in their dominions should stand up which has been ordered to lie down. It is only their soft nature which saves evil from destruction. As the saying is, "We thought it was only an armed horseman. Behold, it is an elephant bearing a tower!"

It is in my mind that the glory of us Rajputs has become diminished since the old days. In the old days, our Princesses charged in battle beside their men, and the name of the clans was great. Then all Rajputs were brothers and sisters. How has this come about? What man of us now relies upon the advice of his womenkind in any matter outside? In this country and in France the women understand perfectly what is needful in the day of trial. They say to their men: "Add to the renown of your race. We will attend to the rest through the excellent education which this just Government has caused us to receive." Thus the men's hearts are lightened when they go to the war. They confide securely in their well educated women. How is it with our horses? Shape and size from the sire: temper and virtue from the dam. If the mare endures thirst, the colt can run without water. Man's nature also draws from the spindle-side. Why have we allowed forgetfulness to impair our memory? This was well known in the old days. In this country arrangements for washing clothes exist in almost every house, such as tubs, boards, and irons, and there is a machine to squeeze water out of the washed clothes. They do not conceal their astonishment at our methods. Our women should be taught. Only by knowledge is anything achieved. Otherwise we are as children running about naked under the feet of grown men and women.

See what our women have already accomplished by education! The Thakore Sahib of Philawat was refused leave from the Government to go to the war, on account of his youth. Yet his sister, who wedded the Rana of Haliana had prepared a contingent of infantry out of her own dower-villages. They were set down in the roll of the Princes' contingents as stretcher-bearers: they being armed men out of the desert. She sent a telegram to her brother, commissioning him to go with them as Captain of stretcher-bearers: he being a son of the Sword for seventy generations. Thus cleverly he received permission from the Government to go. When they reached France he stole them out of the camp, every one of his sister's men, and joined himself to the Rajah of Kandesur's contingent. Those two boys together made their name bright in the trenches. The Philawat boy was hit twice and came to hospital here. The Government sent him a sealed letter by messenger where he lay. He had great fear of it, because what he and Kandesur had done was without orders. He expected a reprimand from the Government and also from his uncle because of the succession. But the letter was an announcement of decoration from the Shahzada himself, and when he had read it, the child hid his face beneath the sheets and wept for joy. I saw and heard this from my very bed in the hospital. So his Military Cross and the rest was due to the Maharanee of Haliana, his sister. Before her marriage she attended instruction in England at the great school for maidens called Ghatun [Girton?]. She goes unveiled among Englishmen, laying hold upon her husband's right arm in public assemblies in open daylight. And Haliana is sunborn.* Consider it! Consider it!

---

*The royal clans of the Rajputs derive their descent from the Sun.

Do not be concerned if I do not return. I have seen all the reports of all the arrangements made for burial, etc., etc., in this country. They are entirely in accordance with our faith. My youth and old age have been given to the service of the Government, and if the Government can be served with the dust of my bones it is theirs. Now that my boy is dead in Arabia I have also withdrawn my petition to the Government for a land-grant. What use? The house is empty.

> Man does not remain in the world
> But his name remains.
> Though Jam and Suliman are gone
> Their names are not lost.

When that arrives, my Maharanee Baharanee will despatch to you *posh-free par parshel-posh* [post-free per parcel-post] my Cross that the Badshah gave me, and a letter from my Captain Sahib's Mother with whose brother I served when I was a man. As for my debts, it does not trouble me in the least that the moneylenders should be so troubled about them. But for the Army and the Police the people would have killed all moneylenders. Give my duty to the Rana of Pech, for his line were my father's overlords from the first. He can hang up my sword beside my father's.

Do not be concerned for whatever overtakes me. I have sifted the sands of France: now I sift those of England. Here I am held in the greatest kindness and honour imaginable by all whom I meet. Though I am useless as a child yet they are unwearied of me. The nurses in my Maharanee Baharanee's Hospital, which is by day a home and a house to me, minister to me as daughters to a father. They run after me and rebuke me if I do not wear a certain coat when it rains daily. I am like a dying tree in a garden of flowers.

THE FUMES OF THE HEART

THE FUMES OF THE HEART

Scene. Pavilion and Dome Hospital, Brighton—1915.

What talk is this, Doctor Sahib? This Sahib says he will be my letter-writer? Just as though he were a bazar letter-writer at home? . . . What are the Sahib's charges? Two annas? Too much! I give one. . . . No. No! Sahib. You shouldn't have come down so quickly. You've forgotten, we Sikhs always bargain. . . . Well, one anna be it. I will give a bond to pay it out of my wound-pension when I get home. Sit by the side of my bed. . . .

This is the trouble, Sahib. My brother who holds his land and works mine, outside Amritsar City, is a fool. He is older than I.

[25]

He has done his service and got one wound out of it in what they used to call war—that child's play in the Tirah years ago. He thinks himself a soldier! But that is not his offence. He sends me postcards, Sahib—scores of postcards—whining about the drouth or the taxes, or the crops, or our servants' pilferings or some such trouble. He doesn't know what trouble means. I want to tell him he is a fool. . . . What? True! True! One can get money and land but never a new brother. But for all that, he is a fool. . . . Is he a good farmer? Sa-heeb! If an Amritsar Sikh isn't a good farmer, a hen doesn't know an egg. . . . Is he honest? As my own pet yoke of bullocks. He is only a fool. My belly is on fire now with knowledge I never had before, and I wish to impart it to him—to the village elders —to all people. Yes, that is true, too. If I keep calling him a fool, he will not gain any knowledge. . . . Let me think it over on

*all sides! Aha! Now that I have a bazar-
writer of my own I will write a book—a very
book of a letter to my fool of a brother. . . .
And now we will begin. Take down my words
from my lips to my foolish old farmer-
brother:—*

"You will have received the notification
of my wounds which I took in Franceville.
Now that I am better of my wounds, I have
leisure to write with a long hand. Here
we have paper and ink at command. Thus
it is easy to let off the fumes of our hearts.
Send me all the news of all the crops and
what is being done in our village. This
poor parrot is always thinking of Kashmir.

"As to my own concerns, the trench in
which I sat was broken by a *bomb-golee* as
large as our smallest grain-chest." [*He'll
go off and measure it at once!*] "It dropped
out of the air. It burst, the ground was
opened and replaced upon seven of us.

[27]

I and two others took wounds. Sweet-meats are not distributed in war-time. God permitted my soul to live, by means of the doctors' strong medicines. I have inhabited six hospitals before I came here to England. This hospital is like a temple. It is set in a garden beside the sea. We lie on iron cots beneath a dome of gold and colours and glittering glass work, with pillars." [*You know that's true, Sahib. We can see it—but d'you think* he'll *believe? Never! Never!*] "Our food is cooked for us according to our creeds—Sikh, or Brahmin, or Mussulman and all the rest— When a man dies he is also buried according to his creed. Though he has been a groom or a sweeper, he is buried like some great land-owner. Do not let such matters trouble you henceforth. Living or dying, all is done in accordance with the ordinance of our faiths. Some low-caste men, such as sweepers, counting upon the ignorance of the doctors here make a claim to be of reputable caste in order that they may get consideration. If a sweeper in this hospital says he is forbidden by his caste to do certain things he is believed. He is not beaten." [*Now, why is that, Sahib? They* ought *to be beaten for pretending to have caste, and making a mock of the doctors. I should slipper them publicly—but—I'm not the Government. We will go on.*]

"The English do not despise any sort of work. They are of many castes, but they are all one kind in this. On account of my wounds, I have not yet gone abroad to see English fields or towns." [*It is true I have been out twice in a motor-carriage, Sahib, but that goes too quickly for a man to see shops, let alone faces. We will not tell him that. He does not like motor-cars.*] "The French in Franceville work continually without rest. The French and the Phlahamahnds [Flamands] who are a caste of French, are Kings

among cultivators. As to cultivation—"
[*Now, I pray, Sahib, write quickly for I am
as full of this matter as a buffalo of water*]
"their fields are larger than ours, without
any divisions, and they do not waste anything except the width of the footpath.
Their land descends securely from father to
son upon payment of tax to the Government, just as in civilized countries. I have
observed that they have their land always
at their hearts and in their mouths, just as
in civilized countries. They do not grow
more than one crop a year, but this is rec-
ompensed to them because their fields do
not need irrigation. The rain in Franceville is always sure and abundant and in
excess. They grow all that we grow such
as peas, onions, garlic, spinach, beans, cab-
bages and wheat. They do not grow small
grains or millet, and their only spice is mus-
tard. They do not drink water, but the
juice of apples which they squeeze into bar-

rels for that purpose. A full bottle is sold for two pice. They do not drink milk but there is abundance of it. It is all cows' milk, of which they make butter in a churn which is turned by a dog." [*Now, how shall we make my brother believe that? Write it large.*] "In Franceville, the dogs are both courteous and industrious. They play with the cat, they tend the sheep, they churn the butter, they draw a cart and guard it too. When a regiment meets a flock, the dogs of their own wisdom order the sheep to step to one side of the road. I have often seen this." [*Not one word of this will he or anyone in the villages believe, Sahib. What can you expect? They have never even seen Lahore City! We will tell him what he can understand.*] "Ploughs and carts are drawn by horses. Oxen are not used for these purposes in these villages. The field work is wholly done by old men and women and children, who can all

read and write. The young men are all
at the war. The war comes also to the
people in the villages, but they do not regard the war because they are cultivators.
I have a friend among the French—an old
man in the village where the Regiment was
established, who daily fills in the holes
made in his fields by the enemy's shells
with dirt from a long-handled spade. I
begged him once to desist when we were together on this work, but he said that idle-
ness would cause him double work for the
day following. His grandchild, a very
small maiden, grazed a cow behind a wood
where the shells fell, and was killed in that
manner. Our Regiment was told the news
and they took an account of it, for she was
often among them, begging buttons from
their uniforms. She was small and full of
laughter, and she had learned a little of
our tongue." [*Yes. That was a very great
shame, Sahib. She was the child of us all.*

*We exacted a payment, but she was slain—
slain like a calf for no fault.   A black shame!
.   .   .   We will write about other matters.*]

"As to cultivation, there are no words for
its excellence or for the industry of the
cultivators. They esteem manure most
highly. They have no need to burn cow-
dung for fuel. There is abundance of
charcoal. Thus, not irrigating nor burn-
ing dung for fuel, their wealth increases of
itself. They build their houses from an-
cient times round about mountainous dung-
heaps, upon which they throw all things in
season. It is a possession from father to
son, and increase comes forth. Owing
to the number of Army horses in certain
places there arises very much horse-dung.
When it is excessive, the officers cause a
little straw to be lit near the heaps. The
French and the Phlahamahnds seeing the
smoke, assemble with carts, crying:—
'What waste is this?' The officers reply:—

'None will carry away this dung. There-fore, we burn it.' All the cultivators then entreat for leave to carry it away in their carts, be it only as much as two dogs can draw. By this device horse-lines are cleaned.

"Listen to one little thing. The women and the girls cultivate as well as the men in all respects." [*That is a true tale, Sahib. We know—but my brother knows nothing except the road to market.*] "They plough with two and four horses as great as hills. The women of Franceville also keep the accounts and the bills. They make one price for everything. No second price is to be obtained by *any* talking. They cannot be cheated over the value of one grain. Yet of their own will they are generous beyond belief. When we come back from our work in the trenches, they arise at any hour and make us warm drinks of hot coffee and milk and bread and butter. May God reward these ladies a thousand times for their kindness!

"But do not throw everything upon God. I desire you will get me in Amritsar City a carpet, at the shop of Davee Sahai and Chumba Mall—one yard in width and one yard and a half in length, of good colour and quality to the value of forty rupees. The shop must send it with *all* charges paid, to the address which I have had written in English character on the edge of this paper. She is the lady of the house in which I was billeted in a village for three months. Though she was advanced in years and belonged to a high family, yet in the whole of those three months I never saw this old lady sit idle. Her three sons had gone to the war. One had been killed; one was in hospital, and a third, at that time, was in the trenches. She did not weep nor wail at the death or the sickness but accepted the dispensation. During the time I was in her house, she ministered to me to such an extent that I cannot adequately describe her kindness. Of her own free-will she washed my clothes, arranged my bed, and polished my boots daily for three months. She washed down my bedroom daily with hot water, having herself heated it. Each morning she prepared me a tray with bread, butter, milk and coffee. When we had to leave that village that old lady wept on my shoulder. It is strange that I had never seen her weep for her dead son, but she wept for me. Moreover, at parting she would have had me take a *fi-farang* [five franc] note for expenses on the road." [*What a woman! What a woman! I had never believed such women existed in this Black Age.*]

"If there be any doubt of the quality or the colour of the carpet, ask for an audience of the Doctor Linley Sahib if he be still in Amritsar. He knows carpets. Tell him all I have written concerning this old lady—may God keep her and her remaining household!—and he will advise. I do not know the Doctor Sahib, but this he will overlook in war-time. If the carpet is even fifty rupees, I can securely pay out of the monies which our lands owe me. She is an old lady. It must be soft to her feet, and not inclined to slide upon the wooden floor. She is well-born and educated." [*And now we will begin to enlighten him and the elders!*]

"We must cause our children to be educated in the future. That is the opinion of all the Regiment, for by education, even women accomplish marvels, like the women of Franceville. Get the boys and girls taught to read and write well. Here teaching is by Government order. The men go to the war daily. It is the women who do all the work at home, having been well taught in their childhood. We have only **yoked** one buffalo to the plough up till now.

It is now time to yoke up the milch-buffaloes. Tell the village elders this and exercise influence." [*Write that down strongly, Sahib. We who have seen Franceville all know it is true.*]

"But as to cultivation. The methods in Franceville are good. All tools are of iron. They do not break. A man keeps the tools he needs for his work and his repairs in his house under his own hand. He has not to go back to the village a mile away if anything breaks. We never thought, as these people do, that all repairs to tools and ploughs can be done on the very spot. All that is needed when a strap breaks, is that each ploughman should have an awl and a leather-cutter to stitch the leather. How is it with us in our country? If leather breaks, we farmers say that leather is unclean, and we go back from the fields into the village to the village cobbler that he may mend it. Unclean? Do not we handle that same thing with the leather on it after it has been repaired? Do we not even drink water all day with the very hand that has sweated into the leather? Meantime, we have surely lost an hour or two in coming and going from the fields." [*He will understand* that. *He chatters like a monkey when the men waste time. But the village cobbler will be very angry with me!*] "The people of Franceville are astonished to learn that all our land is full of dogs which do no work—not even to keep the cattle out of the tilled fields. Among the French, both men and women and little children occupy themselves with work at all times on the land. The children wear no jewelry, but they are more beautiful than I can say. It is a country where the women are not veiled. Their marriage is at their own choice, and takes place between their twentieth and twenty-fifth year. They seldom quarrel or shout out. They do not pilfer from each other. They do not tell lies at all. When calamity overtakes them there is no ceremonial of grief such as tearing the hair or the like. They swallow it down and endure silently. Doubtless, this is the fruit of learning in youth."

[*Now we will have a word for our Guru at home. He is a very holy man. Write this carefully, Sahib.*] "It is said that the French worship idols. I have spoken of this with my old lady and her *guru* [priest]. It is *not* true in any way. There are certainly images in their shrines and *deotas* [local gods] to whom they present petitions as we do in our home affairs, but the prayer of the heart goes to the God Himself. I have been assured this by the old priests. All the young priests are fighting in the war. The French men uncover the head but do not take off the shoes at prayer. They do not speak of their religion to strangers, and they do not go about to make converts. The old priest in the village where I was billeted so long, said that all roads, at such times as these, return to God." [*Our Guru at home says that himself; so he cannot be surprised if there are others who think it.*] "The old priest gave me a little medal which he wished me to wear round my neck. Such medals are reckoned holy among the French. He was a very holy man and it averts the Evil Eye. The women also carry holy beads to help keep count of their prayers.

"Certain men of our Regiment divided among themselves as many as they could pick up of the string of such beads that used to be carried by the small maiden whom the shell slew. It was found forty yards distant from the hands. It was that small maiden who begged us for our buttons and had no fear. The Regiment made an account of it, reckoning one life of the

[41]

enemy for each bead. They deposited the beads as a pledge with the regimental clerk. When a man of the guarantors became killed, the number of his beads which remained unredeemed was added to the obligation of the other guarantors, or they elected an inheritor of the debt in his place." [*He will understand that. It was all very correct and business-like, Sahib. Our Pathan Company arranged it.*] "It was seven weeks before all her beads were redeemed because the weather was bad and our guns were strong and the enemy did not stir abroad after dark. When all the account was cleared, the beads were taken out of pawn and returned to her grandfather, with a certificate, and he wept.

"This war is not a war. It is a world-destroying battle. All that has gone before this war in this world till now has been only boys throwing coloured powder at each other. No man could conceive it!

What do you or the Mohmunds or anyone who has not been here know of war? When the ignorant in future speak of war, I shall laugh, even though they be my elder brethren. Consider what things are done here and for what reasons.

"A little before I took my wounds, I was on duty near an officer who worked in wire and wood and earth to make traps for the enemy. He had acquired a tent of green cloth upon sticks, with a window of soft glass that could not be broken. All coveted the tent. It was three paces long and two wide. Among the covetous was an Officer of Artillery in charge of a gun that shook mountains. It gave out a shell of ten maunds or more [eight hundred pounds]. But those who have never seen even a rivulet cannot imagine the Indus. He offered many rupees to purchase the tent. He would come at all hours increasing his offer. He overwhelmed the owner

[43]

with talk about it." [*I heard them often, Sahib.*] "At last, and I heard this also, that tent-owner said to that Artillery Officer:—'I am wearied with your importunity. Destroy to-day a certain house that I shall show you, and I will give you the tent for a gift. Otherwise, have no more talk.' He showed him the roof of a certain white house which stood back three *kos* [six miles] in the enemy country, a little underneath a hill with woods on each side. Consider this, measuring three *kos* in your mind along the Amritsar Road. The Gunner Officer said:—'By God, I accept this bargain.' He issued orders and estimated the distance. I saw him going back and forth as swiftly as a lover. Then fire was delivered and at the fourth discharge the watchers through their glasses saw the house spring high and spread abroad and lie upon its face. It was as a tooth taken out by a barber. Seeing this, the Gunner

Officer sprang into the tent and looked through the window and smiled because the tent was now his. But the enemy did not understand the reasons. There was a great gunfire all that night, as well as many enemy-regiments moving about. The prisoners taken afterwards told us their commanders were disturbed at the fall of the house, ascribing it to some great design on our part, so that their men had no rest for a week. Yet it was all done for a little green tent's sake!

"I tell you this that you may understand the meaning of things. This is a world where the very hills are turned upside down, with the cities upon them. He who comes alive out of this business will forever after be as a giant. If anyone wishes to see it let him come here or remain disappointed all his life."

[*We will finish with affection and sweet words. After all, a brother is a brother.*]

[45]

"As for myself, why do you write to me so many complaints? Are *you* fighting in this war or I? You know the saying: 'A soldier's life is for his family: his death is for his country: his discomforts are for himself alone.' I joined to fight when I was young. I have eaten the Government's salt till I am old. I am discharging my obligation. When all is at an end, the memory of our parting will be but a dream.

"I pray the Guru to bring together those who are separated.

"God alone is true. Everything else is but a shadow."

[*That is poetry. Oh—and add this,* Sahib.]

"Let there be no delay about the carpet. She would not accept anything else."

THE PRIVATE ACCOUNT

THE PRIVATE ACCOUNT

Scene: Three and a half miles across the
Border—Kohat way. *Time:* The edge
of sunset. Single room in a stone built
tower house reached by a ladder from
the ground. An Afghan woman, wrapped in a red cotton quilt, squats on the
floor trimming a small kerosene lamp.
Her husband, an elderly Afghan with a
purple dyed beard, lies on a native cot,
covered by a striped blue and white
cloth. He is wounded in the knee and
hip. A Government rifle leans against
the cot. Their son, aged twenty, kneels
beside him, unfolding a letter. As
the mother places the lighted lamp
in a recess in the wall, the son picks

up the rifle and pushes the half-opened door home with the butt. The wife passes her husband a filled pipe of tobacco, blowing on the charcoal ball in the bowl.

SON [*as he unfolds letter*]. It is from France. His Regiment is still there.

FATHER. What does he say about the money?

SON [*reading*]. He says: "I am made easy by the news that you are now receiving my pay-allotment regularly. You may depend upon its coming every month henceforward. I have also sent eleven rupees over and above the allotment. It is a gift towards the purchase of the machine needed in your business."

FATHER [*drawing a cheap nickel-plated revolver from his breast*]. It is a good machine, and he is a good son. What else.

SON. He says: "You tell me our enemies

have killed my uncle and my brother, beside wounding our father. I am very far away and can give no help whatever. It is a matter for great regret. Our enemies are now two lives to the good against us in the account. We must take our revenge quickly. The responsibility, I suppose, is altogether on the head of my youngest brother."

FATHER. But I am still good for sitting-shots.

MOTHER [*soothingly*]. Ah! But he means, to think over all the arrangements. Wounded men cannot think clearly till the fever is out of the wound.

SON [*reading*]. "My youngest brother said he would enlist after me when the harvest was gathered. That is now out of the question. Tell him he must attend to the work in hand." (That is true, I cannot enlist now.) "Tell him not to wander about after the people who did the actual killing. They will probably have taken refuge on the Government side of the Border." (That is true, too. It is exactly what they did.) "Even up the account from the nearest household of our enemies. This will force the murderers for their honour's sake to return and attend to their proper business when—God willing—they can be added as a bonus. Take our revenge quickly."

FATHER [*stroking beard*]. This is all wisdom. I have a man for a son. What else does he say, Akbar?

SON. He says: "I have a letter from Kohat telling me that a certain man of a family that we know is coming out here with a draft in order to settle with me for an account which he says I opened."

MOTHER [*quickly*]. Would that be Gul

Shere Khan—about that Peshawari
girl?

SON. Perhaps. But Ahmed is not afraid.
Listen! He says: "If that man or
even his brothers wish to come to
France after me I shall be very pleased.
If, in fact, anyone wishes to kill me,
let them by all means come out.
I am here present in the field of battle.
I have placed my life on a tray. The
people in our country who talk about
killing are children. They have not
seen the reality of things. *We* do not
turn our heads when forty are killed
at a breath. Men are swallowed up or
blown apart here as one divides meat.
When we are in the trenches, there is
no time to strike a blow on the private
account. When we are at rest in the
villages, one's lust for killing has been
satisfied. Two men joined us in the
draft last month to look after a close

friend of mine with whom they had a private account. They were great swash-bucklers at first. They even volunteered to go into the trenches though it was not their turn of duty. They expected that their private account could be settled during some battle. Since that turn of duty they have become quite meek. They had, till then, only seen men killed by ones and twos, half a mile separating them. *This* business was like killing flies on sugar. Have no fear for me, therefore, no matter who joins the Regiment. It needs a very fierce stomach to add anything to our Government rations."

MOTHER. He writes like a poet, my son. That is wonderful writing.

FATHER. All the young men write the same with regard to the war. It *quite* satisfies all desires. What else does he say?

SON [*summarizing*].   He says that he is well fed and has learned to drink the French coffee.   He says there are two sorts of French tobacco—one yellow, one blue.   The blue, he says, is the best.   They are named for the papers they are wrapped in.   He says that on no account must we send him any opium or drugs, because the punishment for drugging is severe and the doctors are quick to discover.   He desires to be sent to him some strong hair-dye of the sort that our father uses.

MOTHER [*with a gesture*].   Hair-dye!   He is a child.   What's he been doing?

SON.   He says he wishes to win favour from his native officer whose white hairs are showing and who has no proper dye.   He says he will repay the cost and that no charges are made for the parcel.   It must be very strong henna-dye.

MOTHER [*laughing*]. It shall be. I will make it myself. A start it gave me to hear *him* ask for dyes! They are not due for another twenty years.

FATHER [*fretfully*]. Read it. Read it all as it is written, word for word. What else does he say?

SON. He speaks of the country of the French. Listen! He says: "This country is full of precious objects, such as grain, ploughs, and implements, and sheep which lie about the fields by day with none to guard them. The French are a virtuous people and do not steal from each other. If a man merely approaches towards anything there are eyes watching him. To take one chicken is to loosen the tongues of fifty old women. I was warned on joining that the testimony of one such would outweigh the testimony of six honourable Pathans. It

[56]

is true. Money and valuables are, therefore, left openly in houses. None dare even to look at them with a covetous eye. I have seen two hundred rupees' worth of clothing hung up on a nail. None knew the owner, yet it remained till her return.'

MOTHER. That is the country for me! Dresses worth two hundred rupees hanging on nails! Princesses all they must be.

SON [*continuing*]. Listen to these fresh marvels. He says: "We reside in brick houses with painted walls of flowers and birds; we sit upon chairs covered with silks. We sleep on high beds that cost a hundred rupees each. There is glass in all the doors and windows; the abundance of iron and brass, pottery, and copper kitchen-utensils is not to be estimated. Every house is a palace of entertainment

[57]

filled with clocks, lamps, candlesticks, gildings, and images."

FATHER. What a country! What a country! How much will he be able to bring back of it all?

SON. He says: "The inhabitants defend their possessions to the uttermost— even down to the value of half a chicken or a sheep's kidney. They do not keep their money in their houses, but send it away on loan. Their rates of interest are very low. They talk among themselves of loans and pledges and the gaining of money, just as we do. We Indian troops are esteemed and honoured by all, by the children specially. These children wear no jewelry. Therefore, there are no murders committed for the sake of ornaments except by the enemy. These children resemble small moons. They make mud figures in their play of men and horses. He who can add figures of oxen, elephants and palanquins is highly praised. Do you remember when I used to make them?"

MOTHER. Do I remember? Am I a block of wood or an old churn? Go on, Akbar? What of my child?

SON. He says: "When the children are not in the school they are at work in the fields from their earliest years. They soon lose all fear of us soldiers, and drill us up and down the streets of the villages. The smallest salute on all occasions. They suffer little from sickness. The old women here are skilful in medicines. They dry the leaves of trees and give them for a drink against diseases. One old woman gave me an herb to chew for a worm in my tooth [toothache] which cured me in an hour."

MOTHER. God reward that woman! I wonder what she used.

SON. He says: "She is my French mother."

MOTHER. What-t! How many mothers has a man? But God reward her none the less! It must have been that old double-tooth at the back on the left lower side, for I remember—

FATHER. Let it wait. It is cured now. What else does he write?

SON. He writes, making excuses for not having written. He says: "I have been so occupied and sent from one place to another that on several occasions I have missed the post. I know you must have experienced anxiety. But do not be displeased. Let my mother remember that I can only write when I have opportunity, and the only remedy for helplessness is patience."

FATHER [*groaning*]. Ah! He has not yet been wounded, and he sets himself up for a physician.

[60]

MOTHER.   He speaks wisely and beautifully.
But what of his "French mother"—
burn her!

SON.   He says: "Moreover, this French
mother of mine in France is displeased
with me if I do not write to her about
my welfare.   My mother, like you, my
French mother does all she can for my
welfare.   I cannot write sufficiently
in praise of what she does for me.
When I was in the village behind the
trench if, on any day, by reason of
duty, I did not return till evening, she,
herself, would come in search of me and
lead me back to the house.

MOTHER.   Aha!   *She* knew!   I wish I
could have caught him by the other
ear!

SON.   He says: "And when I was sent
away on duty to another village, and
so could not find time to write either
to you or to her, she came close to the

place where I was and where no one is permitted to come and asked to see her boy. She brought with her a great parcel of things for me to eat. What more am I to say for the concern she has for my welfare?"

MOTHER. Fools all old women are! May God reward that Kafir woman for her kindness, and her children after her. . . As though any orders could keep out a mother! Does he say what she resembles in the face?

SON. No. He goes on to speak more about the customs of the French. He says: "The new men who join us come believing they are in the country of the Rakshas [Demons]. They are told this by the ignorant on their departure. It is always cold here. Many clothes are worn. The sun is absent. The wet is present. Yet this France is a country created by

Allah, and its people are manifestly a reasonable people with reason for all they do. The windows of their houses are well barred. The doors are strong, with locks of a sort I have never before tried. Their dogs are faithful. They gather in and keep their kine and their asses and their hens under their hands at night. Their cattle graze and return at the proper hour in charge of the children. They prune their fruit trees as carefully as our barbers attend to men's nostrils and ears. The old women spin, walking up and down. Scissors, needles, threads, and buttons are exposed for sale on stalls in a market. They carry hens by the feet. Butchers sell dressed portions of fowls and sheep ready to be cooked. There is aniseed, coriander, and very good garlic."

MOTHER. But all this—but all this is our very own way—

[63]

SON. He says so. He says: "Seeing these things, the new men are relieved in their minds. Do not be anxious for me. These people precisely resemble all mankind. They are, however, idolators. They do not speak to any of us about their religion. Their Imams [priests] are old men of pious appearance, living in poverty. They go about their religious offices, even while the shells fall. Their God is called Bandoo [Bon Dieu?]. There is also the Bibbee Miriam [the Virgin Mary]. She is worshipped on account of the intelligence and capacity of the women."

FATHER. Hmm! Ah! This travelling about is bad for the young. Women are women—world over. What else, Akbar?

SON [reading]. "There are holy women in this country, dressed in black who wear horns of white cloth on their heads. They too, are without any sort of fear of death from the falling shells. I am acquainted with one such who often commands me to carry vegetables from the market to the house which they inhabit. It is filled with the fatherless. She is very old, very high-born, and of irascible temper. All men call her Mother. The Colonel himself salutes her. Thus are all sorts mingled in this country of France."

MOTHER. Ha! Well, at least that holy woman was well-born, but she is too free with her tongue. Go on!

SON. He says: "Through my skill with my rifle, I have been made a sharp-shooter. A special place is given to me to shoot at the enemy singly. This was old work to me. This country was flat and open at the beginning. In time it became all *kandari-kauderi*—

cut up—with trenches, *sungars* and bye-ways in the earth. Their faces show well behind the loop-holes of their *sungars*. The distance was less than three hundred yards. Great cunning was needed. Before they grew careful, I accounted for nine in five days. It is more difficult by night. They then send up fireballs which light all the ground. This is a good arrangement to reveal one's enemy, but the expense would be too great for poor people."

FATHER. He thinks of everything—everything! Even of the terrible cost for us poor people.

SON [*reading*]. "I attended the funeral of a certain French child. She was known to us all by the name of 'Marri' which is Miriam. She would openly claim the Regiment for her own regiment in the face of the Colonel walking in the street. She was slain by a shell while grazing cattle. What remained was carried upon a litter precisely after our custom. There were no hired mourners. All mourners walked slowly behind the litter, the women with the men. It is not their custom to scream or beat the breast. They recite all prayers above the grave itself for they reckon the burial-ground to be holy. The prayers are recited by the Imam of the village. The grave is not bricked and there is no recess. They do not know that the Two Angels visit the dead. They say at the end, 'Peace and Mercy be on you'."

MOTHER. One sees as he writes! He would have made a great priest, this son of ours. So they pray over their dead, out yonder, those foreigners?

FATHER. Even a Kafir may pray, but— they are manifestly Kafirs or they would not pray in a grave-yard. Go on!

SON. "When their prayers were done, our Havildar-Major, who is orthodox, recited the appropriate verse from the Koran, and cast a little mud into the grave. The Imam of the village then embraced him. I do not know if this is the custom. The French weep very little. The French women are small-handed and small-footed. They bear themselves in walking as though they were of birth and descent. They commune with themselves, walking up and down. Their lips move. This is on account of their dead. They are never abashed or at a loss for words. They forget nothing. Nothing either do they forgive."

MOTHER. Good. Very good. That is the right honour.

SON. Listen! He says: "Each village

keeps a written account of all that the enemy has done against it. If a life —a life, whether it be man or priest, or hostage, or woman or babe. Every horn driven off; and every feather; all bricks and tiles broken, all things burned, and their price, are written in the account. The shames and the insults are also written. There is no price set against them."

FATHER. This is without flaw! This is a people! There is never any price for shame offered. And they write it all down. Marvellous!

SON. Yes. He says: "Each village keeps its own tally and all tallies go to their Government to be filed. The whole of the country of France is in one great account against the enemy—for the loss, for the lives, and for the shames done. It has been kept from the first. The women keep it with the men.

All French women read, write, and cast accounts from youth. By this they are able to keep the great account against the enemy. I think that it is good that our girls should get schooling like this. Then we shall have no more confusion in our accounts. It is only to add up the sums lost and the lives. We should teach our girls. We are fools compared with these people."

MOTHER. But a Pathani girl remembers without all this book-work. It is waste. Who of any decent descent ever forgot a blood-debt? He must be sickening for illness to write thus.

FATHER. One should not forget. Yet we depend on songs and tales. It is more secure—certainly, it is more business-like—that a written account should be kept. Since it is the men who must pay off the debt, why should not the women keep it?

THE PRIVATE ACCOUNT

MOTHER. They can keep tally on a stick or a distaff. It is unnecessary for a girl to scribble in books. They never come to good ends. They end by—

SON. Sometimes, my mother, sometimes. On the Government side of the Border, women are taught to read, and write, and cast accounts, and—

MOTHER [*with intention*]. Far be the day when such an one is brought to *my* house as a bride. For *I* say—

FATHER. No matter. What does *he* say about those French women?

SON. He says: "They are not divided in opinion as to which of their enemies shall be sought after first. They say: 'Let us even the account every day and night out of the nearest assembly of the enemy and when we have brought all the enemy into the right way of thinking we can demand the very

people who did the shame and offences.
In the meantime, let it be any life.'
This is good counsel for *us* in our account, oh my mother."

FATHER [*after a pause*]. True! True! It
is good advice. Let it be any life.
. . . Is that all?

SON. That is all. He says: "Let it be *any*
life." And I think so too.

MOTHER. "*Any* life." Even so! And
then we can write to him quickly that
we have taken our revenge quickly.
[*She reaches for her husband's rifle
which she passes over to her son, who
stretches his hand towards it with a
glance at his father.*]

FATHER. On your head, Akbar, our account must lie—at least till I am
better. Do you try to-night?

SON. May be! I wish we had the high-priced illuminating fireballs he spoke
of. [*Half rises.*]

MOTHER. Wait a little. There is the call for the Ishr [the evening prayer].

MUEZZIN [*in the village mosque without as the first stars show*]. God is great! God is great! God is great! I bear witness, etc.

[*The family compose themselves for evening prayer.*]

A TROOPER OF HORSE

A TROOPER OF HORSE

*To the sister of the pensioned Risaldar
Major Abdul Qadr Khan, at her own house
behind the shrine of Gulu Shah near by the
village of Korake in the Pasrur Tehsil of the
Sialkot District in the Province of the Punjab.
Sent out of the country of France on the 23rd
of August, 1916, by Duffadar Abdul Rahman
of the 132nd (Pakpattan) Cavalry—late Lam-
bart's Horse.*

Mother! The news is that once only in
five months I have not received a letter from
you. My thoughts are always with you.
Mother, put your ear down and listen to
me. Do not fret; I will soon be with you
again. Imagine that I have merely gone to

Lyallpur [the big recuiting-dépôt in India]; think that I have been delayed there by an officer's order, or that I am not yet ready to come back.   Mother, think of me always as though I were sitting near by, just as I imagine you always beside me. Be of good cheer, Mother, there is nothing that I have done which is hidden from you. I tell you truly, Mother, I will salute you again. Do not grieve. I tell you confidently I shall bow before you again in salutation. It will be thus, Mother. I shall come in the dead of the night and knock at your door. Then I will call loudly that you may wake and open the door to me. With great delight you will open the door and fold me to your breast, my Mother. Then I will sit down beside you and tell you what has happened to me—good and evil. Then having rested the night in comfort I will go out after the day has come and I will salute all my brethren at the mosque and in the village. Then I will return and eat my bread in pleasure and happiness. You, Mother, will say to me: "Shall I give you some *ghi?*" [native butter]. I will say at first proudly, like one who has travelled:—"No, I want none." You will press me, and I will softly push my plate over to you and you will fill it with *ghi*, and I shall dip my cake in it with delight. Believe me, Mother, this homecoming will take place just as I have described it. I see you before me always. It seems to me only yesterday that I bent to your feet when I made salutation and you put your hand upon my head.

Mother, put your trust in God to guard my head. If 'my grave lies in France it can never be in the Punjab, though we try for a thousand years. If it be in the Punjab then I shall certainly return to it to that very place. Meantime, Mother, consider what I have to eat. This is the true list. I eat daily sugar and ghi and flour, salt, meat, red peppers, some almonds and dates, sweets of various kinds as well as raisins and cardamoms. In the morning I eat tea and white biscuits. An hour after, halwa and puri [native dishes]. At noon, tea and bread; at seven o'clock of the evening, vegetable curry. At bedtime I drink milk. There is abundance of milk in this country. I am more comfortable here, I swear it to you, Mother, than any high officer in India. As for our clothing, there is no account kept of it. You would cry out, Mother, to see the thick cloth expended. So I beg you, Mother, to take comfort concerning your son. Do not tear my heart by telling me your years. Though we both lived to be as old as elephants I am your son who will come asking for you as I said, at your door.

As to the risk of death, who is free from it anywhere? Certainly not in the Pun-

jab. I hear that all those religious mendi-
cants at Zilabad have proclaimed a holy
fair this summer in order that pious people
may feed them, and now, having collected
in thousands beside the river in hot weather,
they have spread cholera all over the district. There is trouble raging throughout
all the world, Mother, and yet these sons of
mean fathers must proclaim a beggars'
festival in order to add to it! There should
be an order of the Government to take all
those lazy rascals out of India into France
and put them in our front-line that their
bodies may be sieves for the machine guns.
Why cannot they blacken their faces and
lie in a corner with a crust of bread? It is
certainly right to feed the family priests,
Mother, but when the idle assemble in
thousands begging and making sickness
and polluting the drinking-water, punishment should be administered.

Very much sickness, such as cholera and

dysentery, is caused by drinking foul water. Therefore, it is best to have it boiled, Mother, no matter what is said. When clothes are washed in foul water, sickness also spreads. You will say, Mother, that I am no longer a trooper but a washer-woman or an apothecary, but I swear to you, my Mother, what I have said is true. Now, I have two charges to deliver to you as to the household under you. I beg you, my Mother, to give order that my son drink water which is boiled, at least from the beginning of the hot weather till after the Rains. That is one charge. The second is that when I was going down to the sea with the Regiment from home, the Lady Doctor Sahiba in the Civil Lines asked of our Colonel's lady whether any of us desired that their households should take the charm against the small-pox [be vaccinated]. I was then busy with my work and I made no reply. Now let that Doctor Sahiba know that I

desire by her favour that my son take the
charm as soon as may be. I charge you,
Mother, upon *his* head that it is done soon.
I beg you respectfully to take this charge
upon you.

Oh, my Mother, if I could now see you
for but half of one watch in the night or at
evening preparing food! I remember the old
days in my dreamings but when I awake—
there is the sleeper and there is the bedding
and it is more far off than Delhi. But God
will accomplish the meetings and surely
arrange the return.

Mother, before going out to the attack
the other day, I had a dream. I dreamed
that a great snake appeared in our trenches
in France and at the same time our Pir
Murshid [our family priest] whose face I
saw quite clearly, appeared with a stick
and destroyed it. Well then, Mother, our
lot went in to the attack and returned from
it safely. Those who were fated to be the

victims of death were taken and those who were fated to be wounded were wounded; and all our party returned safely. At the same time, the Government secured a victory and the Regiment obtained renown. It was *our* horse that went out over the trenches, Mother, and the Germans, being alarmed, fled. We were forbidden to pursue because of hidden guns. This was trouble to us. We owed them much blood on our brethren's account. Tell the Murshid my dream and ask him for a full interpretation. I have also seen our Murshid twice before in my dreams. Ask him why he comes to me thus. I am not conscious of any wrongdoing, and if it is a sign of favour to me, then the shape should speak.

I am quite aware how God rewards the unwilling. He is all powerful. Look at the case of that man of our own family who was ordered to the front with a higher rank. He refused promotion in order to stay be-

hind, and in a month's time he died of the
plague in his own village. If he had gone
to the front his family would have received
the war pension. An atheist never achieves
honour, Mother. He is always unsettled
and has no consolations. Do we Mussulmans think that the Prophet will spend all
his time in asking God to forgive our trans-
gressions? Tell the Pir Murshid what I
have written.

Mother, put down your ear and listen to
me in this matter, my Mother. There is
one thing I wish to impress earnestly on you.
You must know that among recruits for the
Regiment there are too few of our kind of
Mussulmans. They are sending recruits
from the Punjab who were formerly la-
bourers and common workmen. The con-
sequence of this is, in the Regiment, that
we Mussulmans are completely outnumbered
by these low people, and the promotions
go accordingly. Each of our troops, my

Mother, has been divided into two; that is to say there are four troops to a squadron. We Mussulmans should have at least two troops out of the four, but owing to the lack of recruits we have not sufficient men of our faith to form more than one. Now, Mother, as it was in our fathers' time, he who supplies the men gets the promotion. Therefore, if our friends at home, and especially our Pir Murshid, would exert themselves to supply fifteen or twenty recruits, I could approach my Colonel Sahib in regard to promotion. If my Colonel received my request favourably then you at home would only have the trouble to provide the men. But I do not think, Mother, there would be any trouble if our Pir Murshid exerted himself in the matter and if my father's brother also exerted himself. A family is a family even [if it be] scattered to the ends of the earth, Mother. My father's brother's name is still remembered in the Regiment on account of his long service and his great deeds of old. Tell him, my Mother, that the men talk of him daily as though he had only resigned yesterday. If he rides out among the villages with his medals he will certainly fetch in many of our class. If it were fifty it would mean much more influence for me with my Colonel. He is very greedy for our class of Mahommedans.

Mother, our Pir Murshid too, is a very holy man. If he preached to them after harvest he would fetch in many and I should be promoted, and the pensions go with the promotion. In a short time by God's assistance, I might command a troop if sufficient recruits were attained by the exertions of my friends and well-wishers. The honour of one is the honour of all. Lay all this before the Murshid and my uncle.

None of the Cavalry have yet done anything to compare with our Regiment. This may be because of fate or that their nature is not equal to ours. There is great honour to be got out of a lance before long. The war has become loosened and cavalry patrols are being sent forward. We have driven Mama Lumra [a nickname for the enemy] several miles across country. He has planted his feet again but it is not the same Mama Lumra. His arrogance is gone. Our guns turn the earth upside down upon him. He has made himself houses underground which are in all respects fortresses with beds, chairs and lights. Our guns break these in. There is little to see because Mama Lumra is buried underneath. These days are altogether different from the days when all our Army was here and Mama Lumra's guns overwhelmed us by day and by night. Now Mama Lumra eats his own stick. Fighting goes on in the sky, on earth and under earth. Such a fighting is rarely vouchsafed any one to behold. Yet if one reflects upon God it is no more than rain on a roof. Mother, once I was reported "missing, killed or believed taken prisoner." I went with a patrol to a certain place beyond which we went forward to a place which had recently been taken by the English infantry. Suddenly the enemy's fire fell upon us and behind us like water. Seeing we could not go back, we lay down in the holes made by the shells. The enemy exerted himself to the utmost, but our guns having found him bombarded him and he ceased. In the evening we retired out of our shell-holes. We had to walk; it was fasting time and we suffered from thirst. So our hearts were relieved when we returned to the Regiment. We had all been reported to Divisional Headquarters as lost. This false report was then cancelled. The shell-holes in the ground are the size of our goat-pen and as deep as my height with the arm raised. They are more in number than can be counted, and of all colours. It is like small-pox upon the ground.

We have no small-pox or diseases here. Our doctors are strict, and refuse is burned by the sweepers. It is said there is no physician like fire. He leaves nothing to the flies. It is said that flies produce sicknesses, especially when they are allowed to sit on the nostrils and the corners of the eyes of the children or to fall into their milk-pots. The young children of this country of France are beautiful and do not suffer from sickness. Their women do not die in childbed. This is on account of physicians and midwives who abound in knowledge. It is a Government order, Mother, that none can establish as a midwife till she has shown her ability. These people are idolators. When there is a death which is not caused by war, they instantly ascribe it to some fault in eating or drinking or the conduct of life on the part of the dead. If one dies without manifest cause the physicians at once mutilate the body to ascertain what evil was hidden inside it. If anything is discovered there is a criminal trial. Thus the women-folk do not traffic in poisons and wives have no suspicion one against the other. Truly, Mother, people are only defective on account of ignorance. Learning and knowledge are the important things.

Your letters come to me with every mail exactly as if we were at headquarters. This is accomplished solely by knowledge. There are hundreds of women behind our lines who make clean and repair the dirty clothes of the troops. Afterwards, they are baked in very hot ovens which utterly destroy the vermin and also, it is said, diseases. We have, too, been issued iron helmets to protect the head against falling shots. It was asked of us all if any had an objection. The Sikhs reported that they had not found any permission in their Law to wear such things. They, therefore, go uncovered. It was reported by our priests for us Mahommedans that our Law neither forbids nor enjoins. It is a thing indifferent. They are heavier than the pagri [turban], but they turn falling iron. Doubtless, it is Allah's will that the lives of His Faithful should be prolonged by these hats. The sons of mothers who go to foreign parts are specially kept under His Eye.

We know very well how the world is made. To earn a living and bear trouble is the duty of man. If I send you a report that I have won promotion in the Regiment, do not forget to distribute alms to the extent of fifteen rupees and to feed the poor.

Mother, put down your ear and listen to me. There is no danger whatever in box-pictures [snapshot-photographs]. Anyone submitted to them is in all respects as he was before. Nothing is taken out of his spirit. I, myself, Mother, have submitted myself to many box-pictures, both mounted and standing beside my horse. If at any time again the Zenana Doctor Sahiba desires to make a box-picture of *him* do not snatch the child away but send the picture to me. I cannot see him in my dreams because at his age he changes with each month. When I went away he was still on all fours. Now you tell me he stands up holding by the skirts. I wish to see a box-picture of this very greatly indeed. I can read box-pictures now as perfectly as the French. When I was new to this country I could not understand their meaning in the least. This is on account of knowledge which comes by foreign travel and experience. Mother, this world abounds in marvels beyond belief. We in

[93]

India are but stones compared to these people. They do not litigate among themselves; they speak truth at first answer; their weddings are not [performed] till both sides are at least eighteen, and no man has authority here to beat his wife.

I have resided in billets with an old man and his wife, who possess seven hens, an ass, and a small field of onions. They collect dung from our horse-lines upon their backs, a very little at a time but continuously. They are without means of maintenance, yet they do not lay a finger upon any food except through invitation. They exhibit courtesy to each other in all things.

They call me *Sia* [monsieur?] which is Mian [Mahommedan title of respect] and also *man barah* [mon brave?] which signifies hero. I have spoken to them many times of you, my Mother, and they desire I send you their salutations. She calls me to account strictly for my doings each day. At evening tide I am fetched in with the hens. My clothes are then inspected and repaired when there is need. She turns me back and forth between her hands. If I exhibit impatience, she hits me upon the side of the head, and I say to my heart it is your hands.

Now this is the French language, Mother.

(1) *Zuur mononfahn.* The morning salutation.

(2) *Wasi lakafeh.* Coffee is prepared.

(3) *Abil towah mononfahn.* Rise and go to parade.

(4) *Dormeh beeahn mon fiz nublieh pahleh Bondihu.* This is their dismissal at night, invoking the blessing of their God. They use a *Tasbih* [rosary] in form like ours but of more beads. They recite prayers both sitting and walking. Having seen my *Tasbih* these old people become curious concerning the Faith. Certainly they are

[95]

idolators. I have seen the images by the roadside which they worship. Yet they are certainly not Kafirs, who hide the truth and the mercy of Allah is illimitable. They two send you their salutations thus:—*Onvoyeh no zalutazioun zempresseh ar zmadam vot mair.* It is their form of blessing.

She has borne three sons. Two are already dead in this war and of the third no information since the spring-time. There remains in the house the son of the eldest son. He is three years old. His name is Pir, which in their language also means a holy man. He runs barefoot in summer and wears only one garment. He eats all foods and specially dates. In this country it is not allowed to give children pepper or cardamoms. He has learned to speak our tongue and bears a wooden sword which was made for him and a turban of our sort. When he is weary he repairs to the centre of my bed which is forbidden to him by his grandmother of whom he has no fear. He fears nothing. My Mother, he is almost the same sort as my own. He sends his salutations to him. He calls him "My brother who is in India." He also prays for him aloud before an idol which he is taken to worship. On account of his fatness he cannot yet kneel long, but falls over sideways. The idol is of Bibbee Miriam [the Virgin Mary] whom they, in this country, believe to watch over children. He has also a small idol of his own above his bed which represents a certain saint called Pir. He rides upon the ass and says he will become a trooper. I take delight in his presence and his conversation.

The children in this country are learned from their very birth. They go to the schools even when the shells fall near by. They know all the countries in the world, and to read and write in their language and to cast accounts. Even the

[97]

THE EYES OF ASIA

girls of eight years can cast accounts and
those that are marriageable have complete
knowledge of cookery, accounts, and gov-
ernments, and washing of clothes, agri-
culture and the manufacture of garments
and all other offices: otherwise they are
reckoned infirm-minded.   Each girl is given
a dowry to which she adds with her own
hands. No man molests any woman here
on any occasion. They come and go at
their pleasure upon their business. There
is one thing I should like to see, Mother.
I should like to see all the men of India
with all their wives brought to France in
order to see the country and profit by
their experiences. Here are no quarrels or
contentions, and there is no dishonesty.
All day long men do their work and the
women do theirs. Compared with these
people the people of India do not work at
all, but all day long are occupied with evil
thoughts and our women all day long they do

nothing but quarrel. Now I see this. The blame for this state of affairs, Mother, lies upon the men of India, for if the men were to educate the women they would give up quarrelling.

When a man goes out into the world his understanding is enlarged and he becomes proficient in different kinds of work. All that is needed is to show courage. At the present time, one's bravery or one's cowardice is apparent. The opportunities for advancement come quickly. Such opportunities will not occur again.

As for any marriage proposed [for me?] when I return, those things can wait till I return. It is no gain to take into the house a child or a sickly one who, through no fault of her own, dies in bringing forth. If there be any talk between our house and any other family upon this subject they should understand that I desire knowledge more than dowry. There are schools where girls are educated by English ladies. I am not of the sort to make a wedding outside my clan or country, but if I fight to keep Mama Lumra out of the Punjab I will choose my wives out of the Punjab. I desire nothing that is contrary to the Faith, Mother, but what was ample yesterday does not cover even the palm of the hand to-day. This is owing to the spread of enlightenment among all men coming and going and observing matters which they had never before known to exist.

In this country when one of them dies, the tomb is marked and named and kept like a garden so that the others may go to mourn over her. Nor do they believe a burial-ground to be inhabited by evil spirits or ghouls. When I was upon a certain duty last month, I lay three nights in a grave-yard. None troubled me, even though the dead had been removed from their graves by the violence of shells bursting. One was a woman of this country, newly dead, whom we reburied for the sake of the Pity of Allah, and made the prayer. Tell the Pir Murshid this, and that I performed *Tayamummum* [the shorter purification with sand or dust] afterwards. There was no time for the full purification.

Oh, my Mother, my Mother, I am your son, your son; and as I have said at the beginning I will return to your arms from out of this country, when God shall permit!

THE END

THE COUNTRY LIFE PRESS
GARDEN CITY, N. Y.